MW00897689

The Courage To Write

A Collection of Short Stories

by Howie Chan
& Lucien Zeng

Walton Publishing House

Walton Publishing House
Houston, Texas
www.waltonpublishinghouse.com

Printed in the United States of America

Library of Congress Cataloging-in-Publication Data has been applied for.
ISBN : 978-1-7341214-0-7

Dedication

For Josefa and May

Acknowledgements

We would like to express our special thanks of gratitude to Dr. Cheroll Dossett, the strongest and most intelligent person we've ever known, for her encouragement, guidance and support in completing this book. It couldn't be done without her.

Foreword

The Courage to Write: A Collection of Short Stories by Howie Chan and Lucien Zeng, both ages 11 years old, is respectively dedicated to all the young readers and aspiring writers who gave their best; to the parents who gave us the time to rest and instilled in us the faith to master our tests; to the teacher who has been with us through the frowns and the laughs; and to those who have chosen the writer's path.

Table Of Contents

Part I:

Part II:

Part III

Preface
(Letter to Lucien)

Dear Lucien,

The time we've spent together in our shared writing journey was both fun and interesting. We both learned a lot, and we've both seen each other's improvements. You've helped me so much with my creativity. We did everything together—surviving the homework, drawing, writing, and laughing. I will never forget the times we drew a gigantic drawing on the whiteboard when we had a break, did a roleplay, and played weird games with blocks. Over these past three years, we've become closer. With all your imagination and wits, I do not doubt that you'll be a great writer in the future.

Your friend,
Howie

Preface

(Letter to Howie)

Dear Howie,

What an adventure we have been on—climbing over mountains of grammar problems and crossing over the seas of silly auto-corrections! We have come a long way to this day, where we are writing this book. Even though the writing journey is hard, friends make it easier to bear and help us walk further down the path. If we had started alone, this journey would have been a whole lot harder. We have and will overcome any problem we face, past or future.

I'm writing this letter to acknowledge how far we have come in our writing together. I believe that whatever joy or frustration we have encountered, there will be much more of it in the future. Pack your pencil, man your ship, and get ready to sail into a brighter and clearer future.

Your friend,
Lucien Z.

Part I:
Howie's Collection Of Short Stories

The Courage to Write is my first book with my close friend and Co-Author/Illustrator, Lucien Zeng. As you turn the pages, you will begin to understand my story of having the courage to express myself both on paper and through my illustrations. Over the past year, I've noticed how much I love to write and share my stories by reading them aloud both in school and after school.

Sometimes, it was a bit difficult to start writing because I never understood the formula for writing good paragraphs. There were times when I would write without planning. However, over the past year, I have learned that to write longer sentences that connect the main idea to each paragraph, I must always begin with a writing plan. I am fortunate enough to have been taught how to structure paragraphs, so that each sentence connects to one key idea throughout the entire essay.

My first essay is entitled "A Short Story About Courage." It is a narrative essay about a time when I was brave. I am sure you will enjoy reading my essays as much as I have enjoyed writing them for you.

A Short Story About Courage

This is about a time when I acted with courage when dealing with a problem in my life. I had to play and perform the piano on stage for a recital. I was scared and didn't want to perform. My heart thumped louder every time my number came closer to being called. As I waited, I took deep breaths and played my song with my fingers on my lap. Finally, my number was announced, and I stepped onto the stage, bowed, steadied my chair, and started playing. It didn't take long, and I played well.

"Phew!" I bowed again and went offstage.

My heart finally stopped thumping hard after my performance. I pushed through, and that is how I acted with bravery or courage. As you might already know, each of us has to overcome some fears we have in our lives. I have learned that once you do it the first time, it is easier the next time. After I continued to perform on stage, I wasn't scared anymore because I had overcome my fear of performing on stage in front of a crowd.

The Very Special Animal Farm

It was the big day! After waiting for two horrible, treacherous, and antsy weeks, it was finally time to go to the animal farm. When I say animal farm, I don't mean just any boring animal farm. This was the animal farm.

Just recently, a group of explorers unearthed an underground city in China. This vast chamber was full of magical creatures that were hidden from the world since World War One (WWI). Let me tell you how my day started...

I woke up, rolled out of bed, and looked at my calendar on the wall, almost screaming. It was October 14th, and right on that tiny box (still blurry to my eyes because of the sleepiness) was the date with a big, red circle and the words "animal farm" written in the middle. With excitement, I raced to my brother's room and shook him awake.

"Nate, wake up!!!"

He turned his back on me. "Go away, Elaine. It's Sunday."

"Nate... It's animal farm day!" I whispered loudly enough for him to hear. As soon he heard my words, he bounced out of bed and shouted, "YES!!!"

We both charged down the stairs and wrestled each other to brush our teeth first. Once we finished, I raced to my parents' room and yelled, "It's an animal farm day!" Even my dad was excited.

In about 10 minutes, the whole family was ready. We jumped into the car and started driving 65mph on the highway. The car ride there was torture. Every second we spent on the road I felt was being wasted. I won't get enough time to play at the farm, I thought. My mind raced with the cool creatures I would get to see there—centaurs, unicorns, flying pigs; you name it.

"Settle down, dude," Nate said beside me.

"I'm not a dude," I replied.

Then, I looked at myself. I was jumping up and down without

noticing! I forced my bottom to the seat and willed it to stay there until we arrived. My heart was ready to burst by the time we got there.

I looked out the window to see who would be taking us around for the rest of the day, and my heart almost stopped. Standing outside was a striking boy with sleek black hair. His facial features fit him perfectly, and his dark brown eyes seemed to be looking through me. Was he our guide? I wondered. In my mind, I wished and wished and wished. But, he wasn't the only thing I was looking at. I was also looking at the scene behind him.

A group of Alicorns was zooming through the sky, chased by dragons. Elves used goblins as target practice, and a golem wrestled with a Minotaur.

This is crazy, I thought to myself. "Uh... is this a little dangerous?" I asked Dad. "Nope!" he replied. "On the website, they said they found an ancient rune thingy to hold the creatures in check."

We got out of the car, and I could finally see the place more clearly. Scorch marks decorated the grass, and gigantic footprints were everywhere. There were also some big wood shacks where the staff worked. The attractive boy strode next to us.

"Welcome to the first and only magical creature wildlife park. You are now in the bright zones. These are where the creatures of the light live. They like human interaction, but don't make any rude comments at all. If you want more adventure, you can go to the darker fields where darklings make their homes." He walked next to my mom. "And I'm Rex, your guide for your time here. There's only one rule: never go anywhere without a guide. We have the word to destroy any of those creatures. But, they can still kill you." Rex paused for effect.

"So, where do you guys want to go first?"

"Alicorn races!" I yelled.

"Meet the ghosts!" Nate shouted.

"Let's go to the Alicorns, then."

At the Alicorn stables, we got to ride them. I loved the rush of wind in my face, as I flew through the air with narrow misses of rocks and cliffs. It was truly a belly- flopping lifetime experience. After that, we watched a Phoenix reborn, which was cool. It burned up to ash, then it turned back into a bird! That was magical.

Next, we went to see a few more light creatures, and then we set out to the dark lands. Ghosts and mist surrounded us when we stepped in. A Grim Reaper suddenly swooped in, and I yelped. That was such a jump scare!

"Get used to it scaredy-cat. I bet there's a lotta scares in the dark areas," Nate commented.

And, he was right… for once. Skeletons crawled out from graves and tapped me on my shoulders. I kept looking around in every direction while I walked. Cyclopes stared at us with their one eye, creating more tension in the air. I seriously disliked this part of the animal farm. All along the road, I felt like something was going to jump out and drag me away forever.

Finally, we reached the end of the dark zones and saw demons circling the passage with several Chimeras. "You shall not pass!" They boomed.

My heart rate sped up. Was this part of the trip?

"What are you doing?" I asked it, as our guide stepped in front of us. "Blocking you, DUH!"

I really couldn't imagine a demon saying "duh." But, things seemed like they were spiraling out of control. So, I asked, "Is something wrong?" but Rex did not answer. He started to murmur some strange words that I didn't understand. Then, he stopped, and all the creatures guarding the passage went "poof" and turned into green bubbles.

"Okay, let's go," he said. I guess that wasn't part of the tour. We continued to go see more incredible creatures of all kinds. This was the most superb day I'd ever had.

And, the saga continued…

Browntropolis

Animal Farm Revisited

I found myself on a farm. Unusual creatures roamed around me. For a moment I thought where am I? Then, I remembered—the animal farm. I squealed with delight as I walked with the animals of all kinds. When I reached out to touch one, I woke up. My eyes popped open, as I looked around, to see where the animals had gone. The only things I saw were some dirty clothes on the floor with open cabinets and a desk. I sighed.

When am I going to go to the animal farm? I wondered. I looked at my calendar, and my heart skipped a beat.

"Today was the day we were going to the animal farm! How had I forgotten?" I said. I raced out of my room and into the living room to call a family assemble.

"Wake up, everyone!!!" I yelled at the top of my lungs. My parents lounged out to the stairs and looked at me.

"What's wrong?" They asked in a drowsy voice. "It's an animal farm day!" Suddenly, they perked up just like I did.

"Really?" My little sister jumped down the stairs and ran next to me. "Really?" "Yes, Riley. Really." I replied. "So, we better get goin' right?"

So, we did. Everyone was prepared in 10 minutes and zoomed in the car. I had never seen my dad drive so fast. The car was going 80 mph! Even he was excited about the animal farm. My heart raced so fast, I bet it could bounce up to the moon if I had let it go. My little sister jumped up and down for 10 minutes until she fell asleep.

Finally, we reached our destination: The Animal Farm. The setting was incredible. Animals of every kind lounged about, here and there. Our guide stepped in front of our car to open the door for us. Another guide helped our parents out.

"Hi kids! I'm Daniel, and I'll be your guide for today. We don't want to waste any time, so let's get started. What animal do you want to see first?"

"Unicorns!" Riley called out. "Alicorns!" I suggested.

"They're both at the same stables, so don't worry," Daniel said. "But choose your animals wisely, since the boss only allows customers to see three animals."

My sister and I did not change our minds about unicorns and Alicorns. They were the most magnificent creatures I had ever seen. Their fur was white as snow, and they left rainbow footprints wherever they walked. Their one horn radiates a magical barrier that is invisible to the naked eye. Riley beamed joyfully after we saw the unicorns. Of course, I thought, this was every little girl's dream!

Afterwards, we got to ride the Alicorns. Their wings spread out like a blanket over a bed as they soared upwards towards the sky above. The wind flew at my face, making my dark brown hair flying in every direction. "Ahh!!!" My sister screamed, as I whooped. They were making a dive.

Nothing could compare with that force as they spread their wings to stop the fall. Riley's face was green, and she looked like she was going to puke. I laughed.

"Where to next, girls?" Daniel asked.

"Can we watch the ogres fight?" I wasn't sure if there were ogres at the farm. "Sure," he replied.

He led us through a maze of trees, then we emerged in a giant clearing where greenish-gray creatures were fighting. A huge crowd with the worse odor surrounded the arena. The clash of swords made my sister yelp. They were battling to the death. The ogre with its back to us suddenly charged at the other ogre in an act of frustration and anger.

The other ogre moved swiftly and struck down the charging ogre. The crowd cheered. Riley cowered. Then, they started another round. This one was even faster than the last round. It was a giant ogre versus the ogre who'd won the last battle. The giant ogre swung it's club, and the other ogre crumpled. The crowd booed.

"Well, I guess that's enough fighting for today, eh?" Daniel whispered, looking at my sister, who was covering her eyes. "Shall we go to the fairy kingdom?"

"Yes, yes, yes, please!" Riley jumped up and started walking. "To the fairy kingdom, I guess" I responded.

After walking across the forest, over a plain wasteland and a swamp, we made it to the fairies. They were tiny little people with wings flying around. They had some outlandish architecture on their buildings of gold and silver. Many brownies were shuffling around down on the streets while the fairies flew around. The guards at the gate to the kingdom flicked three wands and suddenly we were brownie-sized, too! Faces stared at us as we walked through the plaza. Fairies helped brownies with their needs for magic, and brownies helped fairies with buildings and work.

"They're so organized!" I exclaimed.

"Yes; they are very," Daniel replied. "You should see them build!"

Then, something caught my eye... a skyscraper! Brownies crawled all over it using ladders, fairies, and their ways. I saw one brownie give a list to a fairy, and the fairy made a big pile of bricks for the brownie. Finally, after seeing more fairy- brownie builds, we reached the end of the kingdom.

"Bye, bye, fairy kingdom," Riley said just before we got turned back to our normal size. And, that was it... the end of our tour. We headed back to the gate of the animal farm to meet our parents. This was such an awesome and exotic day for me and my sister.

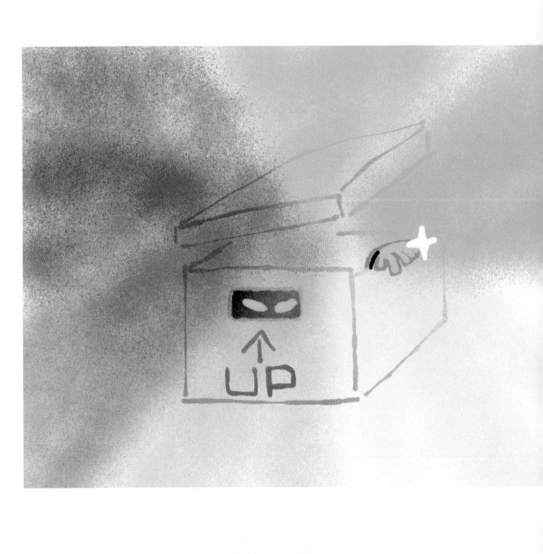

The Box That Talks

Nobody would've guessed that The Box would start talking. It looked like an old book box, felt like an old book box, smelled like an old book box and, even though I'm not sure about this, probably tasted like an old book box, too. Our teacher, Mrs. Poo, had brought it that morning. It did seem like an old book box, right up until Mrs. Poo left the room for a toilet break. But, now that I think of it, I think there might have been some weird symbols on it.

"Keep working on your memoirs, everyone!" she had ordered before she went outside. Mrs. Poo was not forgiving. If we did not obey her, she would just send us to the principal without listening to reason. The principal, however, was nice and never really scolded us or anything.

Maybe she would add something in our report cards, but whoever cares about those? Our parents were the opposite of us. They worried all day about the report cards, as they determined which schools would accept us. The report cards were like judges weighing our education. So, if we couldn't attend a good school using report cards and grades, we would have to go in with pure force. For example, studying all day for math, getting scolded if we didn't know the answer, and so on.

Nobody would want to do that, so back to the point—nobody would want to disobey Mrs. Poo. The classroom was eerily silent for about two seconds before Darius, one of the naughty kids, started throwing pillows around. Julia, Ryan, Kara, and Laura followed his example and got into a pillow fight.

I could understand why. The memoirs were the most boring part of the day— revising and revising and revising. Everyone was on edge from writing for 45 minutes periods. Then, before they could get any crazier with the pillows, the box on Mrs. Poo's desk started beeping. At first, everyone was confused about where the sound was coming from. After a while, we all determined that it came from the box.

I was the first to act. I walked over to the box, where it was beeping and shuffling around. The smell of old books was very overwhelming. The Box also radiated a field of static electricity. I felt my fingers getting tickled and my hair flying around. When I got closer, it stopped beeping and started talking. The air next to the box gave me goosebumps. I wasn't sure if it had to do with the air-con.

"Lemme out! You are a stupid lady! I'll never help you make those no-good missiles!" it shouted.

My first thought was is there a person in there? But it was too small to be a person.

"I don't know where you bought me from, but I'm gonna wreck it just like your lab!"

Was it talking about Mrs. Poo's house? Did she have a lab? I looked at my classmates. They were all staring at me. Neon lights streamed out of the edges of the box, and there was some sizzling. My nose suddenly felt fuzzy. The Box continued talking.

"Arrrghhh!" The Box shuffled and moved with a newfound strength. It was like watching an animal break free. The Box smoked and sizzled. Finally, it fell off the desk and the little tape that held it together broke. A tiny robot flew out of the box, breaking free. It looked futuristic with neon blue armor plating and glowing red eyes. I was surprised that a robot could have such an expressive voice.

"Go die... Wait, you aren't Mrs. Poo?" It looked confused, it's red eyes turning to yellow. All of us gaped at the robot, jaws hanging. No one knew what to do with the robot. I thought about what the robot had said earlier. "I'll never help you make those no-good missiles!" Was Mrs. Poo starting a nuclear war? Whatever she was doing, we couldn't let her get her hands on the robot. Before we could do anything, the door opened, and Mrs. Poo stepped in.

"What's all this fuss about? Why is everyone standing?" Finally, she noticed the robot floating at the back of the room.

"Oh, no," she panicked.

The robot's eyes grew red and pointed it's arm at our teacher. The plating on it withdrew into the arm, where a plasma cannon shot out. It was complete with several tubes that contained purple liquid connected to the cannon. Even though I didn't know what bad stuff Mrs. Poo had done, I couldn't just let her die. My classmates realized this as well because Chris, one of my friends, ran towards Mrs. Poo. I launched myself at the robot, catching it's cannon and raising it upwards.

Boom!

The Air-con on the ceiling was practically vaporized, with bits of the ceiling pouring down.

As my friends ran outside screaming, I grabbed a nearby piece of paper and covered the robot's eyes with it. Then, I took a pair of scissors from the desk, cut all the tubes free from the cannon, and shoved the robot into the box. It moved and struggled, but I quickly closed the lid and sat on top of the box.

"You... don't... understand..." it started saying.

I couldn't hear the rest because the school's alarms started ringing. The school's security charged into the room, carrying bats and shields. When they saw the hole in the ceiling, they moved with more enthusiasm. The school never had any exciting stuff going on, so a hole in the ceiling was already pretty cool.

"What triggered the alarm?" they asked. We all pointed to the box I was sitting on. The security exchanged a look with Mrs. Poo, then took the box. The rest of the day was pretty fun because the teachers were scared that something would fall down from the ceiling, so we spent the rest of the day with another class.

Later that day, when I was leaving school, I saw one of the security people hand the box to a woman in a hoodie. I did not doubt that it was Mrs. Poo. I was tempted to go after her, but I had more important matters on my mind: exhibition. My project was hardly complete, and I had a lot of work to do at home. Mrs. Poo wouldn't start a nuclear war... or, so I hoped.

Welcome To 'Helltists'

Today, when we were driving to the dentist, I noticed that my mom took a left instead of a right. The street we turned onto had a heavy smell of tobacco in the air and swear words flew into my ear. The street was dirty, and armies of rats and mice criss crossed on the sidewalk. There was also weird looking "liquids" splashed on the ground, and some yellow and brown looking thing was spilled out from the sewage hole. We drove past dark mouths of alleys and graffitied walls. People with dirty clothes that looked like gangsters walked around. Dead birds lay on the ground, rotten with flies surrounding them. It smelled so foul, it took all my willpower to not puke. My stomach lurched more the deeper we went. What dentist opens their shop here? I thought.

My mom's face was as tight as mine, and my eyes narrowed. I asked if we were going to the right place. Mom said she was just following the GPS. My heart beat faster and faster. The seconds felt like minutes, and the minutes felt like hours, and the hours felt like days. Finally, we reached an office building that looked weird because it was in the middle of this dark place, like an orange in an apple crate.

We carefully walked out of the car. I didn't know why I closed the door more quietly than normal, as if the monster from "A Quiet Place" was there. The entrance to the building was decent, with glass windows and shiny door knobs. The air was ringing silently as we slipped through the doorway. The lobby was cavernous. The ceiling was high above us, and the sofa looked like I could jump 30 feet high onto it without breaking my legs. I sprinted to the sofa and tried it out. My nerves screamed, "Pain!" when I jumped onto it. The sofa was stone-hard. Just an illusion, I thought, rubbing my knees and hopping off the sofa... just an illusion.

We walked into the tiny elevator, and it barely had space for three more people. My mom looked at her phone. She then pressed the 16th floor. Just before the doors closed, a hand that looked like an ape's reached in and opened the doors again. Mom and I jumped. This was getting scarier and scarier, like a horror movie.

I forced myself to be brave, like the heroes I read about in my storybooks. A raggedy old man with clothes that looked like he had just been in a big battle with a werewolf came in. He smelled of blood. He took one long look at the elevator choices before he asked us, "Are you sure you want to go here?" in his raspy voice that only old men had. His breath was more smellier than the street. Who was he?

"Yes." My mom tried to reply calmly, but the rest of her face betrayed her. The old man tried to talk, but the elevator dinged, and mom lugged me out.

"Use your flashlight!" he called, just before the two metal gates shut, "and good luck!"

I wondered what he was talking about, but as soon as I turned around, I understood. The office was nothing like the rest of the building. The lights flickered and some were smashed on the ground. The furniture was all crushed or broken into pieces. On the lumpy and spiked reception desk, there were some magazines named #BeABadGuy, and torture was on the cover of many of them. The air smelled of rotten pigs, with a tinge of blood. Wait, blood? I thought, then looked at the walls.

The wallpaper had been scratched everywhere, and there were splattered bloodstains. I looked at mom. She was frozen in place. I touched her pulse. It was not beating. Mom was frozen. I heard screams in the distance, with the sound of a chainsaw. Fresh blood trickled down through the doors, then silence. Suddenly, thundering footsteps echoed towards my direction. A demon stepped out from the darkness in the traditional demon form: horns, blood-red skin, glowing yellow eyes, trident, plus a dentist apron. He had gnarled fingers that looked like they had been in the water for an hour and a voice that was surprisingly smooth, despite the form.

"Hi, welcome to Helltists, where we will try our best to torture and rip your guts out without causing any pain." He smiled with crooked, shining teeth.

I pressed the elevator button. "Don't be scared; it's perfectly safe!" he added. As if God was listening to my prayers, the elevator doors opened, and the old man stepped out.

"Come! Quick!" he yelled.

"But—but, my mom!" I protested. Are we going to leave her? I resisted from the old man's grip and tried to take my mom's hand.

"It's too late for her!" he yelled again, grabbing me with his lizard-dry skin. He pulled me in, and the demon smiled as he took my mom with him and walked away. My vision blurred, and the doors shut.

Suddenly, I felt a vortex suck me through thin air, and there I was lying on my bed in the morning with beads of sweat rolling down my cheeks. Just a bad dream, I thought.

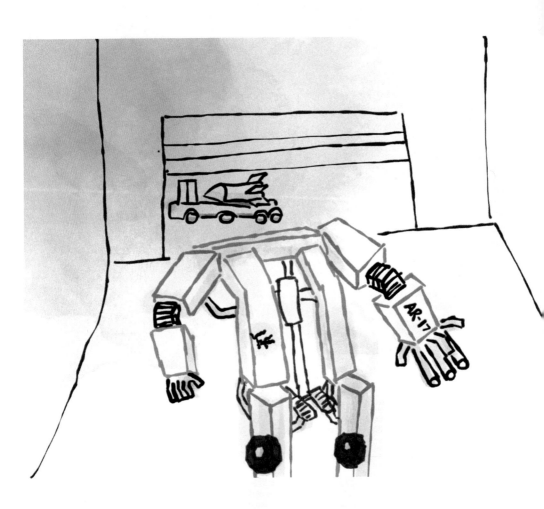

'Escapade'- A Story With Consequences

You might be wondering about that blue color pencil mark in my leg. Yes, that came from a color pencil box in the middle of the aisle and me tripping over it. You would be right about that, but the truth is, that little stab did not make the mark in my leg. Sure, it did go in my leg but, eventually, the dust came out from it, and my leg was fine. Where it came from was the winter holiday after that "incident." Now that I think of it, it was the most fun holiday I'd ever had, apart from genetically enhanced humans, evil masterminds, and the threat of world domination.

This brings us back to three years ago when I was going to Switzerland... I twisted and turned in the sheets, trying to find a way out. My body was even hotter than a sauna. It was so hot! Finally, I found an opening and pushed through; my leg was able to go through the bedsheets. This wasn't the first time I did this kind of stuff. Case in point, there was a time when I twisted and turned so much to get out of the blanket, Mom had to help me. Only this time, I was in an igloo about 2,727 meters up a mountain. It was cool; everything was made of ice, and snow was everywhere. There were only a few things I didn't like, such as the blankets.

I scrambled desperately out of the mattress where the rest of my family members were sleeping—Grandma, two aunties, Uncle, Dad, and mom. I would have to join them later. Right now, my body was sweltering with heat and sweat. I grabbed my heavy-duty jacket and slipped into my heavy-duty pants, then ran outside the ice door... right into the frigid 40-degree weather, where someone bonked me unconscious right there.

When I woke, I found a syringe sticking out of my leg, where the blue dot I have is. I frantically tried to pull it out, but my hands were cuffed to the sides. I started to scream, but a video screen was lowered down to me from a ceiling. It briefly told me of super-enhanced soldiers versus an evil mastermind planning to destroy the world with evil robots. My mission was to attack the enemy base and blow it up. Easy. I don't remember the details, but I think it said the mastermind's name was

Dr. Diabetes. So, now I was getting genetically strengthened. After the video, a robotic arm came up beside me and jabbed me with another syringe. I blacked out once again.

This time, when I awoke, I was in a cargo plane with a bunch of other people from kids to old guys. We were all wearing suits with a machine gun loaded on top. A middle-aged man next to me said, "We're in Antarctic in case you are wondering." Not helpful. Helplessness quickly overcame me as I realized the danger of this mission. We had to fight robots, which means there wouldn't be any mercy on the battlefield.

Before I could figure out any solution to my dire position, the intercom announced that we had t-minus two minutes until drop off. The next two minutes felt longer than my whole life added together. Everywhere I looked, nothing could comfort me. Of course, I thought. This was a war, and the only thing that pushes you on is to be determined... To win. Then, the loading doors at the far side of the cargo dock opened, and wind gushed in. Everyone tensed. After that, the chains buckling us to the seats lifted, and suddenly we were all flying out the plane.

Falling from the plane was a fun experience. I could see the whole snowy battlefield below me, and other planes were dropping off other soldiers. The whole scene looked like it just came out of a movie. Finally, the ground came up to me as I pulled the trigger on my exoskeleton. Some rocket boosters came up beside me and slowed the fall just enough for me to land safely. How did I know how to do that? That wasn't my knowledge.

The snowy ground didn't look as perfect as it did up there. There were charred marks from tracks and large craters from missiles. Everything was surreal. My first enemy came up to me. A giant tank with a giant cannon. It aimed at me, and I just froze. It fired, and the shot was loud enough to wake me back up. I dived towards it. The serum must have developed some new instances because my whole body screamed, "RUN!" However, I dove under the tank with surprising speed and punched upwards. My punch nearly went through the metal. I climbed into the tank where a robot was waiting for me. It looked like a traditional robot—yellow blocky eyes, a gun that comes out from the hand, metal everywhere, and some antennae. My machine gun suddenly snapped to attention and auto fired at the robot. Sparks flew on the walls, floors, and ceiling, but the fight was over quickly. Instead of normal bullets, the gun fired plasma.

Now, to the second phase of the mission: blow up the base. I attached a USB that I pulled out to the control panel of the tank. Once again, not my knowledge. Then, I was driving it towards the base according to the holographic map on my suit. The doors to the base were open, streaming hundreds and thousands of robots. I reloaded the tank ammo, then fired. The shot flew. The bullet glided towards the base in slow motion. I could tell when it landed because there was this explosion that destroyed the doors and most of the robots. I continued to advance. When I looked to the side, I could see that many of my comrades were also taking tanks and standing alongside me.

"Fire!" I yelled into the walkie-talkie.

All of us fired at the same time and demolished the base. The walls caved in, and the mission was complete.

We cheered. Some planes came down and picked us up. Then I was transported back to the syringe room. Suddenly, new thoughts overcame my fear of needles. This war... this was the only action I was probably going to have for my whole lifetime. And in the movies, people usually wipe the soldiers', or the "expendable people's," memories. Or, they kill them.

"Please don't wipe my memory..." I was saying. The robotic arm came up and jabbed me in the leg. When I woke up, I wondered where I was. The plane? The syringe room? Even the tank? But, if I knew about these locations, that meant they didn't wipe my memory. I quietly celebrated.

Later that day, I learned about the results of the war. The news said the icebergs are melting faster. Oh well, I thought, at least this was a long-term problem. If we didn't have that war yesterday, the world would've ended much faster than sea levels rising. Another result, or maybe even a good thing, was actually that the syringe mark would stay with me for the rest of my life.

Questing For Revenge

In the small town of Smallville, there lived a 10-year-old boy named Evan Hawks. Who would have thought he would be become famous for the dumbest act in his life?

"Evan! Time for dinner!" his mom called from the kitchen.

Evan was out again, watching his "adorable" birds. He leaned on the railing of the balcony, looking out at the tree in front of the big brick house. The tree was filled with hundreds of bird species of all kinds. Evan was currently watching a one-eyed, one-legged, and one-winged bird trying to find its mother. Evan sighed. He had to leave again. His father did not tolerate being late for dinner.

He left his post at the balcony and started to walk backward, watching the bird even as he left. Then the bird's mother came. Evan could not miss this moment. He raced back out to the balcony, grabbing his camera as he went. Then, as he got closer to the railing, he realized that he was going too fast. Way too fast.

He tumbled through the air and expected a splat when he landed. He landed on something soft, some sort of cloak or cloth. Then a figure materialized from the thin air, glowing blue.

"Shoot!" he shouted. Evan looked up and gasped.

It was Mr. Pure, the purest villain of all time. "Look what you've done, kid! All these years I've hidden from the police, and now you... argh... You ruined everything!"

Evan started to get up to run, but it was too late. Mr. Pure grabbed his arms, flipped him around to face him, and stabbed Evan in both of his eyes.

"No one will recognize me now," Mr. Pure said, then dashed away.

Evan was going to die. He was going to die. But, he just couldn't admit that truth.

Just before he lost consciousness, Evan saw the mother of the one-eyed bird fly towards him, and everything turned black. He woke up to a voice calling his name. A man with a bushy beard looked at him through very, very thick glasses. He blinked. He was not dead. How? Is this heaven, or hell? Evan wondered. But, he was still in the mortal world.

In the corner of his eye, Evan saw a sign that read: "Smallville Doctor." This was the most expensive doctor in town. If he did not die from blood loss and tissue damage, he would surely die because he was broke.

"Wait. How can I see?" He questioned himself. He noticed his vision was not from his eyes. It was from high above. The vision flew. He was watching himself, from a bird's point of view. From his new third-person perspective, Evan looked very cool. He was draped in a black cloak, wore a black shirt and pants, had a strip of black cloth with a silver eye on it across his eyes, with black gloves and a black scarf.

"Why am I not dead?" Evan asked when he finally got to his feet. "What did you do?" he asked the doctor.

"I did nothing, my dear sir. All I did was make this costume for you. The bird healed you."

Evan took a moment to process the info. He was alive. He lost his eyes; yet, somehow, he could see through a bird's eye. How did the bird heal him? "Is this a spirit animal relationship?" he wondered. He could deal with that, though he would prefer to be his old self.

"Where is Mr. Pure?"

The man looked confused. "There is no Mr. Pure here." "But... but... Where are my parents?" he asked.

"You have no parents. You are an orphan."

Evan finally understood. That dreaded Mr. Pure had poked out his eyes, killed his parents, and did a memory wipe on the whole town. He would get him.

"Can you teach me how to use a spirit animal relationship?" Evan knew the answer to this question before he asked.

"No, no, no. You need to rest! After an injury, all patients need to rest before they do anything else."

"I can't. Okay?" Evan replied, desperately, "I don't have much time..." "Nope! I have to follow the rules."

"Let me learn about spirit animal relationships." Evan spat the words out, sounding out each syllable. As he said the sentence, his hand started glowing dark and light blue. His new eyes/vision watched himself curiously.

"Fine!" The doctor took out an ancient, colossal book from the shelf. "I can teach you all you want."

Over the next few hours, Evan learned about how to attack with the bird, how to defend, and how to spy.

They had finished the book. "That is all," the doctor informed.

"I am ready." Evan packed his luggage and set out for revenge on Mr. Pure. It will be easy. Now that he still had a memory of the villain's clothing and whatnot, he could find him easily.

"Wait! What about my fee?" The man cried from the doorway.

"I'll give you the money for the clothes after I'm finished with my... uh." Evan looked for the word that could describe his journey, "my quest."

"Remember; okay?" the man requested, still looking anxious.

"I will!" Evan put out a blanket on the road with some beggars. No one would suspect him now. He quickly turned his vision into the bird's and telepathically told his partner to fly around and look for a person who fit the description he'd given. His bird flew around Smallville's perimeter and surrounding area but found no traces of Mr. Pure. Oh well, he thought. I'll have to do it the old-fashioned way. He had the choice to teleport, but it would take him a large amount of energy, so he did not.

Evan quickly went to a barn and bought a horse with the remaining money he had. He rode hard, stopping every 10 minutes to scan the perimeter with his bird. The landscape was beautiful with sky blue and a clash of a mixture of green, blue, and orange. There wasn't much civilization in those parts of the world.

When he rode into the small town, he found one person who had seen Mr. Pure pass by. Evan thanked him, then turned west and rode harder. He eventually reached the mountains of doom, where he found magical blast traces, footprints, and the blood of animals. It was a big chance that was Mr. Pure.

After night fell, Evan rolled out a mattress and continued to search with his mind. His bird was soon exhausted and both of them rested for the night. The next day, after an hour of searching, he found the place where Mr. Pure was hiding. Evan snuck in without much trouble. There, inside Mr. Pure's base, was a labyrinth of caves with dripping wet puddles everywhere. Not a single decoration was in sight.

Then, a voice boomed, "Greetings, dear traveler... due to your unfortunate luck, you have somehow wandered into the base of Mr. Pure. Death will approach shortly." While he was talking, Evan led his bird through the caves and into Mr. Pure's room. It was the only room with furniture. A large golden carpet was on the ground, and the walls were made of obsidian.

There was a chair and a table in the center of the room. Mr. Pure sat there, smiling the biggest smile ever. You won't smile for long, Evan thought.

He grabbed a dagger, teleported next to the villain, and dispatched the vile man swiftly.

Mission complete. Evan teleported back to his home where everything was suddenly turned back to normal. His parents came out of his house, hugging him close.

"Where have you been?" they asked. "Long story," he answered.

Everything was back to normal, except for his eyes. To be honest, he kind of liked his new powers.

Kai Ping Field Trip

As soon as I woke up, I was excited. We, all the people in fifth grade, had been awaiting this day for an entire month. We would get a field trip. Even though it only lasted two days, we didn't have to go home! Two days without school, and instead of parents who ordered us around, we were surrounded by friends! It was a day where all of us would rather have school than a holiday (other than Dariush, who was absent on purpose).

I thought about the trip the whole time during the drive to school. Worries and doubts and happiness and daydreams all bunched into one giant ball. Our teachers told us the day before that we should not be late to school and to report to the MPR (multi-purpose room) as soon as possible. When I got there, I had expected to see a crowd like in a popular theme park ride, but there were just a few kids standing around. This was no surprise; I was a teacher's son, and I always arrived early.

I walked into the huge room. One of the teachers there, Ms. Elliot, told me to put down my bag and to sign up for my activities. "Only sign for two, one on day one and one on day two!" she ordered.

I looked the list over. There was one for musical... Chinese instruments, one for visiting the villages in Kai Ping, one for making dumplings, and three more that I forgot. I signed up for the first two. Soon after, the crowd started to file in. It was chaotic while everyone signed up for their activities. My friends and I talked for a while, and it was soon time to say bye to my mom. I waved to her when I had the chance, and my heart felt more quenched with each step I took. This would be the longest time I had spent by myself without my parents. The big ball of thoughts I had grew bigger and bigger, but when the bus left school, I put all those behind and focused on the present.

We had only one-stop on the whole trip, which was a large gas station in the middle of nowhere. On the bus, we played a game I made up to kill time. After two hours— that felt more like four—we arrived at the first checkpoint: a museum where we learned about Kai Ping culture and stuff.

Most of us thought it was boring. Afterwards, we went to the place where we would be staying that night, it was a hostel! Basically, it's a hotel without room service, but it is pretty nice. Our teachers rented the whole place, so we didn't have to worry about being quiet and bothering any other guests.

We then had recess, which also seemed "boring" in most of our minds. There wasn't any equipment that we were used to at school, but we still had friends, which prevented this period from being "very boring." When I think about it, it wasn't as bad as the bus ride—which counted as "super boring."

The rest of the afternoon was for our activities, but first we had to visit and tour a rich guy's garden. It was entertaining, as our tour guide was experienced, and there were not many barriers that kept us from walking around the garden by ourselves. My friends and I stayed behind, going into every building and often stopping to take selfies with the camera of one of my friends.

Finally, we went back to the hostel and ate lunch. It was so good. I had a bunch of pork, rice, egg, lettuce, and meat in my mouth, so I didn't talk much when we were eating.

Next, it was time to do our activities. Other groups left the hostel, but we stayed behind. About 20 old women and men came to perform, and we got to play a string instrument with only two strings. It was hard to make real musical noise with it, though the men played it with precision. The dance wasn't that impressive, but we still got to try it. That was easier than trying to play the instrument. They repeated some steps, and soon our small group mastered the little dance.

At first, when they told us to come and try, no one went up. But the second time, our teachers ushered us up on stage, instantly whipping out their phones to record us. It wasn't as "fun" and "awesome" as I'd expected, but it was good enough to qualify as "okay."

We had free time in the hostel and had a pillow fight in our room. I didn't eat as much dinner compared with lunch, but I still finished half a bowl to stop the TA's (teacher assistants) from complaining. While we were eating dinner, Ford, one of my friends, tried to get Alfred and Kanji (more friends) to drink his cup of water, which ended in one successful try out of two.

Before long, it was time for bed. The teachers let us play for a while longer, and that's when the first problem occurred. We had taken one of my roommate's candies and were passing it around, when the roommate (I'll not say who) finally burst and punched me in the head. I had a long cry, and all my friends were angry with him. I didn't get a chance to report it, as all the teachers were already in their rooms. Later it was rumored his mom had a long talk with him about anger management. But, back to the story.

The troubles continued. Brian, Lucien's friend (I'm pretty sure you know who Lucien is; hint Co-Author.) started singing dumb versions of real songs. For example, gummy bears were trying to attack you in one song, and animals were peeing on your shoe in another. There were many different varieties, but they all had one similar effect: annoying everyone in the room, so we couldn't sleep. He set a bad example for Eric, a Chinese friend, who started to tell stupid jokes.

All of us who were trying to sleep, finally burst. We all screamed at them, but it only made them happier and more eager to talk. The commotion signaled Ms. Trobridge. She stopped by and scolded us for being so loud. As she was talking, I was thinking of how many circles would be under my eyes in the morning after her long talk.

"I could hear you down the hall!" she spoke in a quiet, but a harsh voice. Ms. Trobridge lectured us a while longer, then left. We didn't speak anymore after that.

The next day, we finished all our activities, all the tours, and left at one o'clock in the afternoon. I left our room both happy but sad. Happy because I didn't have to sleep with Brian again, and sad because it would be some time before I would sleep with six people together again.

When we arrived back to school, all the parents were awaiting our return. We climbed off the bus and finished our field trip of a lifetime. We didn't have to worry about school the next day, as our trip was on Thursday and Friday, so it was time for the weekends. It was four days off from school and, just to tell you, this qualified as "awesome."

The Sleepover

It was a cold and stormy night, and Peter Auxier was heading to his friend Mike's house to have a sleepover. It was late past ten, and Peter didn't know why Mike told him to come so late in the night! They wouldn't even have time to play and watch movies. Thunder boomed in the distance. Then, it started raining. Peter quickened his pace and started jogging. The bushes next to him on the sidewalk shuffled.

"Gah!" Peter jumped onto the driveway. It was slippery and wet, and seeing the dead cockroaches on the road wasn't helping. The streetlights on both sides of the road all snapped shut, as though something had turned them off. It's okay, Peter thought, the streetlights just close earlier, that's all. He was two blocks away from Mike's house. Then, behind the house he was next to appeared some footsteps... coming towards him. Peter ran to Mike's house and opened the door.

"Mike!" Peter shouted, "There's a person, or a monster, or whatever chasing me and..." he was cut short when he noticed that Mike's house was empty and dark with no light. Maybe he went to sleep already, Peter thought, as he trudged up the stairs. The stairs creaked on every step. Creak, creak, creak... Peter reached the top of the stairs and peeked into Mike's room... also empty. His heart beat faster every second. Something tapped him on his shoulder.

"Ahh!" Peter jumped and tumbled down the stairs. "Ha!" Mike jumped down the stairs with a grin.

"You should've seen that look on your face!" he said. "Yeah!" Another voice came from the door.

"Oh, that's my brother."

"So... all this was a prank?" Peter asked, still terrified about what happened. "Yes!" Mike said, "Were you scared?"

"Well..." Peter didn't want to be a scaredy-cat. "I gotta go to the bathroom first." He walked inside the bathroom with no intent to pee. Yes, he thought, I was scared.

The Importance Of Taking Action

People who want something badly enough should take some action. The importance of action is to be more independent. The purpose of this essay is to describe the importance of taking action for the following reasons:

- You can get what you want.

- You can achieve your goals.

- You can improve your health.

- You can make your family proud.

Taking action will help you get what you want. Let me give you an example. I remember the time when I wanted a LEGO set. My parents said I had to memorize and play a song with the flute. So, I took action to get the LEGO set. Eventually, I completed my task and got my prize.

Taking action can help you achieve your goals. This is slightly different from getting what you want because goals are more personal. Getting what you want is more of a prize. An example of achieving my goals is when I wanted to finish all the books in a series. I had to take action to read books every single day, every chance I got. (This may have caused me bad eyesight, but at least I achieved my goal.)

The third reason action is important is because you can improve your health. Before, my air and lungs weren't strong. I usually coughed after doing sports, but after I took action and started swimming, my health improved.

Lastly, taking action is important because you can make your parents proud. While I am doing the activities I listed above, my parents were proud of me for memorizing my song, finishing so many books, and swimming so well. Action is critical to our lives, and even though your action is small, you can make a big difference.

My Ideal Teachers

What is your ideal teacher? In this essay, I am going to write about mine and reasons to support it.

The first trait I need my ideal teacher to have is that he/she must have a system for teaching. Why is a system important? Because I had a German teacher who had zero experience in teaching. As if that wasn't bad enough, he also did not have a system, so with every lesson he jumped from this chapter in a book to a random page that was printed. The lessons made my head hurt so much that, eventually, I decided to quit.

The second trait I need my ideal teacher to have is to speak a language I know. Once, I had a math teacher who came from Spain. Mom and I decided to try out the teacher because all her friends were saying the teacher was good; it was the exact opposite. The teacher's English was very bad and, even though she taught okay, I couldn't understand what she was saying, and it made me very confused. Mom and I didn't take any more lessons from her.

The third trait he/she has to have is to be kind. A teacher who isn't kind and doesn't care about me is not a good teacher, nor is this an ideal trait. Even if he/she teaches very good, I won't feel very good about it. I had a teacher in elementary school who was not kind, and no one in our class liked her. We all loathed going to that class.

Lastly, my ideal teacher needs to scold me or, in other words, help me to focus. A teacher who just chills and lets me do anything isn't good. He/she wouldn't teach me anything, and I wouldn't learn anything either. These are the traits my ideal teacher must have.

Part II:
Lucien's Collection Of Short Stories
Letter Of Introduction

Lucien Zeng is 11 years old. He was born in Hong Kong and holds both Canadian and Hong Kong passports.

Lucien is a sixth-grade student at the prestigious American International School of Guangzhou. His favorite hobbies include playing tennis, and he enjoys surfing. Although he is not a fan of sports

activities that cause him to heavily perspire, Lucien has more of a penchant for reading and writing, particularly lyrical poems that rhyme.

Most notably, Lucien has an animated personality most of the time, and his combination of wit, charm, and his love for making friends provide the wonderful combination for Lucien to entertain readers and listeners with his stellar storytelling skills. His reading voice is magical, and he can sing, too!

Lucien is a non-native speaker and writer, and it is his love for the English Language that prompted him to write a book for other non-native speakers. He wants to encourage them through the art of Storytelling that there is a great sense of satisfaction and joy, which writing brings to him because he can capture his imagination on the page. Along with his original illustrations, Lucien makes his stories aesthetically pleasing to the eye.

More importantly, Lucien's ability to write narrative essays has a wide range of topics including, but not limited to, fantasies, science-fiction, historical fiction, biographies, etc. He has earned himself the reputation as one of the few young writers, along with his co-author and illustrator, Howie Chan, to become the two top writing students in his grade at the American International School of Guangzhou.

In closing, Lucien adds that he is proud of the three-book projects that were compiled in fourth grade two years ago. Each book project evolved into a better version of his writing style, which served as the basis for his most recent compilation of short stories in The Courage to Write.

Courage

Oh, villainy! Oh, fair!

What are thou Courage?

Thy Courage leaping off unknownst cliffs?

Thy Courage punching villains with thy fists?

What art Courage, you say?

You say Courage isn't leaping off unknownst cliffs?

You say Courage isn't punching villains with thy fists?

You say Courage art conquering thy feeling's heart,

Thy Courage art capturing thy brave in thy heart,

Thy Courage letting thy fear lest.

Is that what courage is?

Or, art there more?

That is for you to find out... In the future, you must go.

Lucien 2019

Animal Farm

I was peacefully sleeping in my comfortable bed when "boom" a portal appeared. I fell through, screaming... I landed gently onto something soft. I sat up dazed, looking down at my feet to see what I had landed on. It looked like grass, but the color was... what? Purple? On what planet is the grass purple?

Looking around nervously, I saw that beside me was a tree. It looked like any other tree, so I was momentarily relieved. However, all feelings of relief washed away and were replaced by waves of fear when I saw what was growing on the trees.

There were monsters growing on the trees—banshees, dragons, trolls, you name it! I figured I broke the limit on how fast a human could run when I took off like lightning in the opposite way of the monstrous trees. After what seemed like hours, I stopped to see if the monsters were following me. I took my first breath when I figured out that I couldn't see a single living soul within a mile radius. Just when I was about to relax, I heard a loud thumping in the distance, getting closer and closer. I peered into the distance to see what it was and, with my great horror, it was a bull! Its horns were as sharp as swords, and its body was thicker than a redwood tree. Its red eyes glared menacingly at me! I stood paralyzed, unsure of what to do. The bull got faster, as it stampeded towards me with hatred showing in it's evil eyes. When I was sure the monstrous bull was about to impale me, a voice woke me up.

"Hello. Hello. Wake up, Hucien! It's almost time to go!" Lowie shouted, as he shook me out of bed.

I had remembered! Me and my brother, Lowie, were going to a farm for the whole day!

Lowie was almost jumping out of his pants when I couldn't be lower than a withered plant.

"Hmm... What time is it?" "Almost 10."

Holy cow! We were leaving at 10:05am! I immediately jumped out of my bed and did everything quickly, although now

49

I can't remember all of the details of what happened that morning.

I brushed my teeth so quickly, I'm sure they almost fell out, and I ate my cereal as fast as a boy living in Canada (as fast as a sixth grader could ever eat). I had to jump into the car as we drove off.

"Mom?" I asked nervously, "What farm are we going to?"

"Nothing much; just an old animal farm called Hablefaven . It's only for a day, after all." Yeah right. Just for a day... I thought.

"Have fun!" Mom shouted over the whirring of the engine and the screeching of the wheels as she drove away. Lowie and I stared at the giant sign that

said: Hablefaven, just a normal farm with no strange animals that would like to eat you!"

"Gee, the caretaker here mustn't have much creativity," I said, as we slowly walked to the entrance.

"What's a caretaker anyway?" Lowie asked.

The front gates were already behind us. "It's a person who is in charge of the farm, doofus." I replied, feeling smart.

A lady came out of a nearby house to greet us.

"Hi, gentlemen!" the lady cheerfully said. "You must be Hucien and Lowie! Welcome to Hablefaven!"

She led us through a gate that was labeled "Don't Go Farther Gate" and then down a dirt path through another gate, and another, and another, and another.

"Umm, Miss..." Lowie began. "Miss Sendra, will do fine."

"Miss Sendra, why are there so many gates?" Lowie asked.

"The caretaker here, Keth, likes to feel secure." Ms. Kendra said, flatly.

We walked across the simple dirt path that was suddenly surrounded by trees. I could swear it took hours from the dirt road to get to the end, and then we reached a crossroads. There the path split into three different roads—one going right and made out of shiny golden bricks, the second leading forward (covered with flowers and all kinds of fresh fruit), and the third going left (laced in red and surrounded by images of war).

"These are the three main roads of Hablefaven," Ms. Sendra continued, "the one on the right leads to the cabin, the one that goes forward leads to the barn and fields, and never, never follow the path that leads left, for reasons only Keth knows."

"I wonder what's behind the left path?" I whispered to Lowie, as we followed Ms. Sendra down the path with golden bricks. "I think it's actually where the caretaker, Keth, keeps all his money."

"I'm not sure," I shrugged. "I mean, the red paint and pictures look pretty convincing..." the yellow brick road eventually turned and then displayed a wide variation of houses. It ranged from houses made of dirt to mansions made of jewels. We then stopped in front of a regular bungalow.

"This is where you are living today." Ms. Sendra told us.

"Why can't we live in the other houses? They look so cool!" Lowie moaned.

"They are reserved for... other residents." Ms. Sendra said. "Go unpack your belongings and meet me back outside for your first task of the day".

We unpacked our belongings, used the facility, and met Ms. Sendra outside. We walked out of the yellow brick road and into the crossroad.

"We should make a break for the red road, who knows what riches lie beyond?" I whispered to Lowie. He nodded in agreement. We suddenly bolted for the red road. Ms. Sendra screamed behind us, but we didn't listen. The further we went into the road, the denser the forest became. We ran and ran until we realized we were lost.

"Uh-oh," Lowie said.

"Look! I see something!" I pointed at the red glow in the distance.

We walked toward it. It was a big book sitting on top of a lectern.

The book's title was: "Tales of Howie Chan; Advice and Stories on Life; X-treme addition!" I flipped open the book. I was suddenly overwhelmed by memories that weren't my own. A person sitting in a dentist's chair surrounded by green smoke. A person battling a creepy clown with a sword, and even a kid who was hanging by his underpants on a metal pole! With all these memories, I fainted. The last thing I remember was the red glow of the book.

Courage

Some people have severe health problems, but they still find the courage and strength to live successful and happy lives. Today, I'm telling you a true story about myself dealing with problems in courage. This happened in 2016 in Boston, Massachusetts in the United States of America.

I was going to have my eye surgery because my left eyelid was lower than my right eye. I was nervous. We arrived in the hospital early that morning, and we saw the sunrise from the waiting room. The room was quiet because they put the TV on mute, and we were the only family there. The nurse asked us to wait. We waited and waited, and I walked around in the room again and again until my name finally called.

We entered a big room full of curtains and equipment. I changed my clothes; the nurse did some checks on me; and, the doctor came by and asked me to relax. I was taking a deep breath, but I was still nervous because it might hurt, and I worried whether the doctor could ease my pain. When my parents and I were talking, one nurse brought an iPad to me. "Hurray!" I played iPad games in the surgery room.

Playing games made me forget about the surgery, and I felt the surgery room was not a horrible place anymore. After about 15 minutes, a nurse brought some small bags of juice and asked me to choose. I chose my favorite (strawberry flavored) and the surgery began. When I woke up, my parents were beside me. I felt weak, thirsty, and tired. The nurse said I could eat a popsicle, but my mom said no. Sigh...

Luckily, the TV had Disney Channel. I watched some cartoon movies before leaving the hospital. The surgery was over, and I wasn't worried anymore. People thought I was a brave boy after the surgery. I think you can be as brave as me by just doing a few activities below:

Taking a deep breath, walk around, taking another deep breath and playing iPad games... it's that simple!

Last and the most important is that I have a happy family, and my parents will always be with me, my whole lifetime!

First Trip To Laos

My name is Lucien; I'm from Pack 5858, the Cub Scout located in Guangzhou, China. In November 2018, my mom, as a Den Leader, organized our Den to Laos—the first trip for all of us to Laos ever. The trip was one of the most interesting ones in life. It was unique because all the events that happened in Laos were new to me.

When we first knew we would go to Laos, some of us were worried. Because, we learned from the books and media that more than half of Laos' people are still facing poverty. The country also lacks hygiene and medical supplies. Only half of the kids can go to school because most children live in isolated villages. All of these facts had brought doubts about our trip. However, in the end, the trip has brought an exciting and memorable experience to all of us.

It was a four-day trip to Vientiane, the capital city of Laos. The events included: hiking in the national park, teaching and sharing in the local school, visiting local garment factories, cooking local Lao dishes, visiting local silk workshops, and local sightseeing. One of the most memorable times to me was hiking in Vientiane's National Park. Vientiane has a tropical climate, so even in November it was still hot (33 degrees Centigrade, 92 Fahrenheit); it was really hot. I was nearly burning during the long and exasperating walk through the mountains of green and the forests of bamboo. I was so tired, and even a bit angry about why we had to hike there, but the promise of rest kept me going.

Thinking back, I was glad I went on that hike. Apart from the long and exasperating road we had to walk on, we got to see many exotic and wild animals, such as pink dragonflies, blue dragonflies, red dragonflies, monarch butterflies, a spider on it's hypnotizing web, and a cave full of yellow butterflies! We also experienced big and red lumps after being bit and stung by the red and yellow ants in the forests when we stood still, not moving for a few seconds. Along the way, we also learned a lot about plants—which ones were poisonous, which ones grow fruits and flowers and in what season, different bamboo species, tropical pines, bamboo orchid, and some leaves that are edible, like a ginger leaf.

After we waded across a wide river, we had a break for lunch at a beautiful waterfall, and some of us got to swim in it! On the way out of the national park, we picked up some trash in the forest. The hiking was about four hours in the national park, and it brought more enjoyment than frustration to all of us.

Another memorable event was our visit to a local school named "Angels for Children." It might not be as exciting as it sounds, but it marked my "first-ever teaching experience," which I would remember in life. I had the pleasure of teaching the local students in middle school; although, it was not as easy as it sounds. First, you had to teach them for 1 ½ hours! A few minutes is easy, but it's hard to keep the audience entertained for such a long time. Secondly, they were middle schoolers (13-14 years old)! It can be challenging to teach someone older than you! And, last but not least, most of the students spoke only a little English and couldn't understand Chinese at all; and, even their teacher spoke basic English, nothing fancy! How was I supposed to teach someone whom I could barely communicate with? Just thinking about it made me nervous.

We (WEBELOS 2 scouts) were divided into five groups, with two of us teaching one class. My friend Brian and I spent one week preparing for this 1 1/2-hour class, and you know what? My best partner lost his voice due to a bad cold, and he could barely talk! It sounds funny, but seriously, it wasn't funny to me at all. When the day came, I steeled my nerves and went to teach the class. I was calm and clear- minded when facing all of them. Guess what? It turned out to be okay. They listened carefully, eager to learn and actively took part.

Through the class, we showed them how to draw comics, introduced the Boy Scout Salute and Oath, also and taught them how to do it in Sign Language. At the end of class, we taught them an English song. From this event, I have improved my public speaking by a significant amount; I have also learned how to engage the audience and manage their expectation and response on-site. I am also better prepared for an event like this in the future. I hope in the future you will get to have an educational trip like mine, for it will teach you a lot.

Before we left school, we were surrounded by students asking when we would go back again. From their eyes, I saw purity, kindness, curiosity, and joy. I felt so lucky for everything my family has provided to me, and I wish I could do more for those kids. The trip has ended, but the memory stays. It has made me a stronger scout and a better person.

Ideal Teacher

My idea of a perfect teacher is the teacher needs to be smart. If the teacher isn't smart, he or she can't appealingly teach information. A teacher also needs to be humorous. A lesson would be so interesting if everyone is howling from laughter! What's a good teacher if he or she isn't open-minded? That way, a teacher could come up with creative activities for the students to enjoy! As a side note, all the points I've talked about so far would have a better effect on students if the teacher was also handsome!

The teacher I'm talking about today is one of my favorite teachers, Mr. Phillips. He matches my description of an ideal teacher. Mr. Phillips interestingly teaches hard subjects. I didn't like math until he came along! He used interesting tactics to get us to learn math. For example, there were fun games, worksheets, and apps we liked to use. By doing the math and enjoying it at the same time, we remembered it quicker and better. At the same time, Mr. Phillips liked to make jokes. He made all of us students laugh and turned any frown upside down! One of the jokes he used almost every day was, "You have diarrhea of the mouth!" He says this sentence every time we talk too much in class.

Mr. Phillips makes up games that are fun and educational at the same time! One of the games was called "Country Trading." We were in groups, and we had to trade with other groups to get the resources needed. Then, we cut out shapes to make money. Mr. Phillips put some random items into the game. However, he didn't tell the group he gave it to what it was for, only to another group who didn't have it. It was so interesting, the whole class begged Mr. Phillips to let us do the game again! From this game, our class learned how to value resources and earn money.

Lastly, Mr. Phillips is handsome and sporty. That's because... well, his face is perfectly proportioned, and his muscles add to the effect. He gained those muscles from playing basketball every Tuesday night. In conclusion, from what I've written today, I can assume Mr. Phillips is my idea of an ideal teacher. He is smart, humorous, open- minded, and handsome, which fits my description. Therefore, I believe right now Mr. Phillips is the best teacher for me. I hope I can meet a teacher as good as Mr. Phillips in the future.

Penny-Wise

It was late one cold, stormy night... nearly 1:00 am in the morning. The last of the lamps were about to flicker out. "This is it," a voice said, as he crept down the stairs. "I have been waiting for ages for this moment," he spoke.

He snuck down the hallway and towards the door. He had been planning this moment for a long time. He had almost everything he needed. There was no stopping now, as he had gone too far. "Can't turn back now," he muttered.

He got the machine on his 13th birthday and, from that day on, he knew he needed to try it. However, the landlord had said no. Now, this was it; he knew it. "This can't fail," the voice said, as he opened the door. A sudden gust of wind blew inside. It almost knocked him over, but he knew he couldn't stop because of the weather. He stood up, and another gust of wind flew inside. This time, he was still standing. Rushing out the door. For a moment, all this was too good to be true...

Howjien was finally going to fly a kite! He had been waiting so long for this moment! Although he might have not chosen the best weather, he couldn't wait much longer! He ran down the front steps and into the rain, not caring about the cold.

"Finally, I get to fly a kite!" Howjien exclaimed. He unwrapped his kite; it was still in its wrapping paper! He let his kite fly into the dark, gray sky. It wobbled for a second or two but eventually came to a stable state. Howjien laughed and ran down the street. He couldn't believe it; Howjien was finally flying a kite!

He arrived at the park. "Hurray! The park!" he shouted, but then he remembered it was already 1:34 in the morning, so Howjien kept quiet. However, his kite flew up and into a tree! He went over to the tree. It was a small one, but big enough to be taller than he was. Howjien jumped and tried to reach his kite, but nothing worked. Just as he was about to give up, a clown appeared on the tree! Howjien wasn't scared. After all, what can a clown do?

"Excuse me," Howjien said. "Is there a circus nearby? Because I would like to see it."

"There is no circus around here child," the clown replied.

There is something weird about this clown, Howjien thought, and I need to know why. "Just give me my kite," Howjien said impatiently.

"I will, child; believe me. But first," the clown said, as he started to pull out something, "why don't you have a balloon?" he asked, pulling a balloon out of the tree.

Howjien liked balloons, but he wasn't going to take one from this weirdo! "Ehh... Sorry, got to go to the bathroom," he said and then rushed to a neighbor's house.

Howjien rang his neighbor's doorbell. "Why, hello Howjien. What's the matter?" Howjien's neighbor, Ted, asked.

"There's... a... clown... in... a... tree..." Howjien replied nervously, not sure what to say.

"Oh, really? Then, let's go take a look. Shall we?" said Ted.

Howjien secretly smiled. That clown is in for it now! he thought. However, when they got there, the clown was gone.

"Oh well, I guess he went home," Ted said and then went home himself. Once he was out of view, the clown appeared again!

"You think puny humans could stop me?!" the clown shouted.

"No... I mean, yes," Howjien tried to sound brave, but at heart he was terrified. "I've had enough trouble for the day; take your kite back," the clown said, as it pulled the kite out of the tree.

Howjien took it and started to walk back home. Five minutes passed. Strange, thought Howjien, it doesn't usually take that long. Ten minutes passed. "Something is going on here, something very weird," said Howjien. Four days passed, and Howjien still hadn't made it home, nor did he faint from hunger or thirst. Then, he finally got it. It was the clown that had made this happen! He grabbed a piece of wood and stole some metal from a shop. (It was ok since the spell made everyone disappear.)

Howjien carved the metal into a long, triangular shape. Then, he tied a piece of wood and metal with some rope. At last, Howjien was ready to confront the clown. It didn't take too long to find the tree. This time, the clown was standing on the ground... with a sword 2 ½ feet long.

"So, you have come back," the clown said. "I'm ready for you, now," Howjien replied.

With that, they suddenly crashed into an epic sword fight. However, in the end, the clown pinned Howjien to the floor.

"Ready to give up now?"

Howjien gave no reply. Instead, he quickly round-house kicked the sword out of the clown's hands, and then he pinned the clown to the floor saying, "We will meet again; I promise!" With that, they both disappeared in a puff of smoke.

THE END

Robot And Human

In the infinite abyss of the universe, there is a galaxy called the Milky Way. It is the most ordinary galaxy you can imagine. In that galaxy, there are many stars, planets, and solar systems. In one of the solar systems, there is a planet called Earth. Long ago, humans ruled this planet but now—because of technology expanding too far—it has caused the robots to rule over humans. Let's get to the robot's perspective and find out what's going on:

"What is that?" I asked Patrick 553, as we walked to work. "I've seen it somewhere… I think." replied Patrick.

"I think it's called a human," said Leonardo 674. "Well, I think it's an alien," I replied.

"It's not an alien. It's a human. Remember?" asked Patrick hopefully. "Yeah, they created your great-great-grandfather and mother.

"Remember?" mimicked Leonardo.

"Yeah, right. This vulnerable, fleshy, no-physical-protection weakling created us? Like, I'm supposed to believe you?" I shouted.

"Hey, calm down dude. It's not like we just sided with them, right?" Patrick said, as he tried to calm me down.

"Yeah, I guess you're right," I said. Then, we continued walking down the street. See how civilization has become? Now, let's see the story from the human's point of view:

"I just don't understand why those robots keep staring at me. It's not like I am carrying a bomb on my back. Sure, I may be the last human alive, but that doesn't give the robots a reason to stare at me all the time.

They stare at me when I am asleep; they stare at me when I am awake; some of them even stare at me when I'm in the shower! I guess when you're a robot, there are no "private parts." I spend most of my time begging for food and money.

There's nothing else much to do when you want to get a job, but the moment the shop owner sees you are human he or she says no. That is the reason I am so poor and barely surviving."

Questions to consider:

- Do you see a different perspective?

- How different they are?

- Can you see similarities in their perspectives?

- Do you think the human should be treated nicely, or do you think the human should be left where he is? Why or Why not?

Saturday

If you ever find yourself hanging from a large metal spike by your underpants, five meters above the ground in a top-secret military base, and your only hope of going down safely is this kid who cares more about what you do than you, you've got to be asking yourself, "Gee, how did I get into this wonderful situation?" Yeah, that was what I was thinking, too.

Well, at least all of this won't be in the newspaper, since you're at a military base! Okay, you probably want to rewind a bit. Let's all go back to this morning...

It was a Saturday (aka the glory day), where Monday is more than 24 hours away, and you get to sleep in and wake up late. I thought it was going to be a good day, and it was! Just before my friend, Hermes, got an idea. You see, Hermes is tricky. He can be a good friend but in difficult circumstances. Well, let's just say he can turn the tide really fast.

After breakfast, I met Hermes to hang out. I was just starting to talk about the latest movie when he said, "Hey, I've got an idea."

When Hermes gets an idea, you should run away ASAP, but I listened. Probably the worst decision I've made in my entire life.

"This is how it's going to work," Hermes grinned. "Your dad works in the military, right? Of course, I'm right. Anyway, we're going to sneak into the military base, record a YouTube video, and become rich and famous."

"I don't think..." I started.

"Hmm, you're right. I don't think we're going to get rich, just famous. Come on! Now or never!" he shouted, as he ran down the road.

I sighed as I followed him.

It was approaching evening when we finally got to our destination—a fully guarded military base. I was looking forward to going home, but Hermes had other ideas.

"You got that key?" he whispered. Oh, how tempted I was to say no, but I reluctantly gave the keys to the military base over to Hermes. Then, he slowly walked towards the locked gate door with lots and lots of warning signs around it. He put the key into the keyhole, and after a few seconds, the door swung open.

"The-stupid-person-who-is-going-to-get-us-all-killed first," I said to him.

He went in, and after a few seconds of reconsidering running home, I followed. "Where shall we film the video?" Hermes questioned.

"I know a good spot," I piped up. "It's on top of the HQ." How I would have regretted those words later, I had not known then.

Hermes broke into a grin. "Now, we're talking! Let's go!"

I slowly climbed to the top while Hermes zoomed up like Spiderman. After we got up there, Hermes started filming. I was more concentrated on the view. However, a watch guard from a nearby watchtower shone a light in my face and shouted, "Hey, what are you doing?"

In confusion, I backed up a step and fell off the roof into a metal spike, thus ripping my pants. I hung from a large metal spike by my underpants, five meters above the ground in a top-secret military base, and my only hope of going down safely was this kid who cared more about what I did than me. That's how I got into that situation. Then, I fell and died. (Just kidding! However, I would've preferred that to what happened next.)

"HELP ME! HELP ME! HELP ME! HELP ME! HELP ME!"

I screamed at Hermes.

"Oh, my gosh guys, look! This is the horrible torture the army does to people! That kid is going to fall to his death anytime now!" Hermes commented as he pointed the camera at me.

"Please, people who are watching this video. Leave a like, subscribe and hit the bell, and this boy will live!"

I was dying of embarrassment from both the idea of Hermes posting this video, and also that people might see I'm so pathetic that

I was being socially embarrassed by a non-living thing.

Luckily, the metal spike came to my rescue. It broke in half, and I fell down and away from the camera view. Before I passed out on the floor, I had just enough time to hear Hermes say, "See! He fell because you didn't like and subscribe!"

The rest of it was a blur. After I got out of the hospital, I was grounded for two months and had to accept extra homework. I never saw Hermes again, and I never went on YouTube again either.

The Box That Talks

If you can learn anything from this story, you are a freaking genius. I wrote this story because the local public library needed one more book to beat the genius world record. I'm just going to put a fancy cover on it, send it to my friend to do some editing on it, and then mail it to the library, and BANG! Instant hundred dollars for me!

Anyway, this is a non-fiction story and non-fiction stories are important, so here goes: On one particularly sunny morning at Blankmind Elementary School, I was sitting at my desk. I know. Not interesting. However, just then my class's teacher, Ms. Carnage, walked into the classroom. Wow, an average school with teachers and classes in it. This is getting exciting! Just you wait! Instead of going over the usual boring lectures about how slavery is awesome, and Hitler was sane, she plopped a big, wooden box on the table.

The sound was loud enough to make everyone shut up. Then, without another word, Ms. Carnage walked out of the classroom. We waited in silence for about five seconds. Then, the whole class erupted. People were flipping desks over, whacking each other, and shooting spit balls everywhere. I took cover in one of the corners inside the classroom and covered myself underneath a beanbag for protection. I also took the big wooden box with me, just in case I needed an extra shield, or I need to resort to violence.

After the anarchy waged on for about a minute or so, the box started to rustle and creak. I didn't want a swarm of bees or enraged badgers in my hands, so I threw the box as far into the class as I could. Turns out, I had a good arm. The box knocked two students unconscious and smashed a table. When I thought it would just land on the ground, it landed in the middle of the classroom, which was also where somebody put a 2-liter water bottle. The water bottle was smashed and sent the water flying and hitting whoever wasn't behind somebody. That got everybody's attention. They all looked at the box. It was rumbling more violently than ever before. Everybody started whispering and wanted to know:

- What's inside the box?

- Who threw the box?

- Is it cheeseburgers?

- Why did the teacher bring it in the first place?

- Is it going to destroy the world?

- And, of course, is it cheeseburgers?

Suddenly, the box exploded. Not the suspense you're looking for? Well, too bad! All sides of the box came flying off, and black smoke started pouring out of it. Everyone screamed and ran in different directions, bumping into each other, and screaming some more. I even screamed. When nobody was noticing, a figure walked out of the shadows. When we finally noticed, it was too late.

"Hello," the figure said. "I am Nyan Cat."

Meanwhile, while we were distracted and dragging our jaws around on the floor, all the black, churning smoke had transformed into bright and colorful rainbows. When we finally turned around, everything was cheerful and friendly and represented optimism. The figure that was standing there had also changed. Before it was nothing but a misty shadow, and now it was a giant, cute cat with a giant pop-tart as a body.

After five minutes, someone managed to get their mouth fixed and asked, "Who are you, and what do you want?"

Nyan Cat just meowed. Nothing happened. Then Nyan Cat sighed and said, "Look; I don't have much time here, so just get on with it. Introduce yourselves. What's your name? It's Jimmy. Don't be so surprised! I can read minds! I can also do a bunch of other stuff, too. I'm a genie, but a cat. Have you seen any of the seven wonders of the world? I'm all over them! The Nazca lines were dedicated to me, but the priests kept on getting it wrong! That's where the "monkey" and the "bird" comes from! Have you wondered how King Tut died? He was driving his chariot around when bang... He hits me right in my belly. You can probably guess what happens next. The Mayan empire got deserted because one of them tried to eat my body! Can you believe it? I had no choice but to destroy everything, so that scenario doesn't happen again.

Anyway, since I'm here, I will grant the next person three wishes if he or she can guess what I'm thinking. Ready? Setty? Goooooooo!"

It took us 10 seconds to process all the information, and everyone surrounded Nyan Cat, bombarding him with answers, but everyone's reply was, "No."

Finally, when everyone else was deep in thought, I approached Nyan Cat and said, "You are thinking of how nobody will guess what you are thinking of."

At first, there was silence. Then, Nyan Cat grinned. "You win! However, I never said when you would get the wishes! HAHAHAHAHA! So long, suckers!" Then, he/she/it flew out the window. That was the last time I have ever seen Nyan Cat again.

The Foreign Country I Want To Go To Most

I have been to many places. Japan, Korea, Thailand, Australia, New Zealand, Spain, Portugal, and America are all one of them, but none can beat Canada. Canada beats all the rest of the countries because the wildlife is much more plentiful, which means I get to study them. Also, the weather is much clearer and healthier, which gives an energized body.

Canada is known to have wildlife roaming around. Where else are you going to find moose crossing the road? Or, rabbits in the park? Or, geese in public ponds? Or, deer in your backyard? Or, squirrels on the roof? Sure, America has them, but Canada has much more of a variety of animals since Canada can hospitalize animals that enjoy the colder temperature. Also, because of the wide range of different animals, school projects about ecosystems and animals will be much easier to do. Because of this, I won't have to spend all day after school—working on projects and homework—and, therefore, have more time to myself! Other benefits include pet prices would be cheaper due to the gigantic range of animals. More animals mean more life forms to spread seeds from plants, which results in more trees, bushes, and other greenery, which ends up with more plants to create oxygen, and finally leading to having more oxygen, which means a healthy body for everyone.

Having a clean atmosphere is important. Fortunately, in Canada, we have just that. A blue sky with a side of white clouds and a blazing sun are more important than you think. For example, when walking down the street in a gloomy mood, when it's a beautiful day outside, the sun can shine optimism onto everyone and put them in a good mood.

Second of all, a clear day means there's no pollution wafting around, so you have a low chance of getting ill. Fewer people being ill means fewer people visiting the hospital, which means the doctors and nurses get some free time of their own!

Also, because of the beautiful day, people like to go for a walk in the local parks, which means park owners earn more money. Also, taxi drivers will earn more money because, usually on this day, people would like to go to a remote outdoor area to hike and camp. Getting there usually takes a long time, so people prefer to take a taxi over having to drive there themselves.

I like Canada over anywhere else I've been to because of its plentiful wildlife and its clean atmosphere. After reading this article, I hope you can take a vacation to Canada sometime in the future. Who knows? Maybe you might decide to write a recommendation letter about Canada, too.

The Time When I Completed Something Hard

As soon as the teacher said the words, "You're dismissed," I was the first one out the door. I grabbed my snack from inside my backpack and started for the stairs. The hallways sped behind me as the wind blew in my face. Before I knew it, I was facing the playground and eating my snack. I watched as the smaller children filed into the school building while more familiar faces flooded out. My friend, Brian, sneakily walked towards me. Of course, I didn't know this, but when Brian finally said, "BOO!" I didn't budge. I turned around and replied, "Hi."

Brian sat down next to me. "Man, one of these days I have to scare you." He sighed. I said nothing for a few seconds, then I reminded him, "Eat your snack quickly; that means we have more time to play."

The rest of my friends came down the stairs. They were all crowded around each other, talking about Pokémon cards and some junk food. We agreed a long time ago we would all meet near the ping-pong table at recess, and that's exactly what my friends and I have been doing for roughly three years. We've always come here to talk and to eat our snacks before we go out into the playground to play. However, more recently it has changed. We had come here to do something else during our free time. I was surprised to see them come down so quickly today. Their teacher thinks the students should go to recess at the time where the rest of us should be already at recess. We barely managed to make a circle that was big enough for what we were going to do, and then one of my friends, Galen, pulled out a box.

Inside of this little black box was a game. The game was based on a warring period in China and was a card game. We enjoyed it because one, it was fun and competitive, and two, our parents approved of the game because it's all Chinese, and we can get a chance to learn the language. If you think about it, parents rarely approve of a game kids like to play, but that's not related to what I was talking about. Anyway, the game started as usual.

You pick your character (randomized); you get a random identity, which tells you who's your teammate (also randomized); and, finally, you get your playing cards (I'll let you guess if it's randomized)... I started to play with enthusiasm, confidence, and joy. I thought in my mind I have to win this, yet time and time again, I have failed. Until one day, I said to myself, "I will win this round."

The snack time started like every other one: finished class, went downstairs, finished snacks, and friends come. However, when it was time to play, another student called Carson wanted to play! It seemed alright at first, but someone said that if we let Carson in, it would go beyond the player limit. Someone suggested that I go out, but luckily, my good friends came to my aid and supported me. In the end, Carson got bored with seeing us argue and went to play ping pong instead. That meant we could continue with our game, and we did just that. We played for a long time, even longer than usual. By the end, it was just me and my opponent, facing off against each other. In normal circumstances, I would've lost, but yesterday at home, it turned out my mother and father used to play the exact game when they were my age as well! They gave me a lot of useful tips, so I cleaned the table with my opponent that round. You might argue this isn't a worthy achievement to write about, but it was my achievement, and that means a lot to me.

The Worst Day At The Dentist

It all started one day when my mom took me to go to the dentist for our monthly checkoff. "Comm'n, now," Mom said, as we were driving in the car. "The dentist isn't so bad."

"Yes, it is!" I grumbled.

"If you think that it's not bad, it won't be!" Mom encouraged me.

For the rest of the trip, I sat quietly in the car, hoping some miracle would come by. It didn't. After a 10 minute drive, I reached the building where the dental office was located. The tower was grey and had eroded to almost nothing but steel frames. It smelled like a vulture pooped there and then died on the roof.

When I reached to open the almost useless doors, the handle popped off and hit my feet, making me wince in pain. My mom and I walked to the end of a long hallway that started by the door and ended by the elevator. We pressed the button and waited five minutes for the elevator to come down to the first floor. When it opened, a rancid blast of onion fart came rushing out. I almost fainted when it hit me. Mom and I went inside and was immediately engulfed by the stench. If I had stayed there for long enough, I would've fainted and went to the hospital to avoid the dentist, but noooooo. Just about when I was going to faint, the elevator door luckily (or unluckily) opened. I stepped outside and told myself it was going to be fine. Then, the elevator door closed, and I was in complete darkness.

The pitch-black room I stood in was horrible beyond description. Even the devil would have puked if he was in that room. I'll try to explain it to you, but you'd have to be there to know it. It's like the quote: "If you weren't there, no words can describe it. If you were there, no words are needed." Anyway, the room was pitch- black with no windows.

It smelled like someone died there and came back as a zombie and died again. I had come here many times, but each time when I was finished, my mind instantly forgot everything about here because it was so anxious to get rid of the bad memories. I touched the walls, as I started down towards the waiting room (for that was one of the procedures I remembered to do). The walls were cracked and hard and fell off as I touched them. After walking a few more unsure meters, I got to the waiting room. It was more of a random chair room than a waiting room.

Chairs were facing each other, stacked on each other, glued to each other, taped to the walls, and a lantern dangling on a chair on the roof made it so I could see all the chairs in their glory. I settled on one of the less corrupted chairs and started waiting.

Waiting in the waiting room for too long might have ended in another elevator accident; the smell would've overpowered me, and I would've fainted. However, a nurse who looked like she could beat Hulk in hand-to-hand combat came in after a few minutes and grumbled, "You're next."

She led me down a dark hallway to an ominous dark oak door that was spilling green smoke out of its cracks. The door suddenly slammed open and broke into tiny pieces, while the green gas started pouring out like water. "Come in, Come in. I've been expecting you," a voice said that sounded like scratching fingernails on a blackboard. My eyes were as wide as dimes at that point. I would've run, but the gigantic nurse pushed me in, and green smoke covered up the entrance as if it had never been there.

The green smoke then cleared a path towards a suspicious-looking dentist chair. I glanced around me for escape options, but there was green smoke everywhere except the path and the chair. I slowly walked down the path and grudgingly laid down on the chair. It felt like needles went through it, and it was made out of leather (or some sort of skin). I smelled something as soon as I sat on the chair. It smelled like the overuse of cologne and rotten flesh. Then, I remembered; it was the smell of the dentist!

At that moment, I wished I could have a time machine. I would've gone back in time and made sure all this never happened, but alas, nobody in the whole world has a time machine. The dentist appeared out of the smoke and, boy, did he look creepy! He was skinny—almost only bones. He wore leather shoes and long black pants, a black coat, and a top hat. He looked like a cross between a zombie and a gentleman.

"Well then," the dentist smiled, "I didn't expect you here!" More smiling, and all I could do was whimper. "Let's check your teeth." The dentist grinned and took out tools that looked like torcher machines. "Open wide!" he said, still smiling.

I opened wide because I didn't want to turn to shish kebab. The dentist put the tools in my mouth. They tasted like rusted metal dipped in blood, but I didn't dare move because I swore I heard the nurse's drool drip onto the ground, as she was thinking about her next dinner. After what seemed like an eternity, the dentist pulled the tools away and said, "My, my... Looks like you need to have a tooth pulled out!"

I whimpered in protest, but the dentist said, "Now, now... It won't hurt a bit!" Then, he pulled out a giant tweezer and reached into my mouth, and I heard a pop...

That's all my friend Herman said he could remember from his trip to the dentist's office. Then, he said, "Hey, aren't you going tomorrow?" That's when I knew I was in for a real nightmare.

The Craziest Pet

I usually don't like to write. I would rather be outside exploring in the woods or playing video games than writing. Then again, what I'm going to tell you (or write to you) is too weird and too complicated for one person to keep in their head. My name is Cetrix Appleseed, and I am about to tell you about the weirdest day of my life.

I like animals—a lot. That's where my mom got the idea of getting me a pet, so I wouldn't have to go into the forest to see animals. Mom told me about this, and I said, "Why not?" We started to organize a place for the first pet in our house when I asked, "What pet are we getting?"

My mom and I spent 10 minutes thinking about what pet we should get. Then my mom suggested that I go to the bookstore and buy a book she saw that might help. She said the author's initials were L.H. We were lacking ideas then, so I followed her advice and went off to find the book. Turns out that finding one single book was harder than I thought.

I arrived at the bookstore all optimistic and confident, but that soon turned to pessimism. I learned the hard way that there are many, many authors whose initials are L.H. There were Lucie Herman, Locklin Howdo, and Lulu Harvey. Seriously?

What kind of name is Lulu Harvey? Anyway, I found the book I think my mom was talking about. It was called Tales of Howie Chan, Advice and Stories on Life by Lowie Hucien. The author's name was even worse than Lulu Harvey in my opinion, but it seemed helpful, so I bought it.

I then went to a nearby park and sat on a bench and started reading. I checked the table of contents and flipped to the page where it said Pets: Which One is For You? It said in the book if you are a wilderness person, the best pet is an exotic one, for that is what your spirit wants. I decided to give it a shot. I first called my mom and said I'll be going to the pet store. Then, I started walking to the pet store. Around an hour later and after much walking, I finally reached it.

It's supposed to be called a pet shop I thought, as I walked through the antique doors. Behind the counter inside stood an old man. "How may I help you today?" The old man smiled.

"Do you have any exotic pets?" I replied with no facial expression. "Certainly! We have one last one!"

The old man smiled again and walked into a dark room. After a few seconds, he came out holding a parrot that was bright purple with red and yellow spots all over it. "This certainly is... exotic," I said without blinking.

"Oh, yes, it is! The parrot is 50 bucks."

So, I paid up and left the pet store. I put the parrot in my backpack, so people wouldn't tease me about it, and I started walking home. The first weird event happened not long after I left the pet store. I was walking back home, thinking of where I was going to put the parrot when a dude wearing sunglasses, who was driving a Lamborghini, pulled up to me and said, "Yo, can I have that parrot in your backpack?"

I was really surprised, but I said, "How do you know there's a parrot in my backpack?"

The guy nervously looked around and said, "Look, I need the..."

He suddenly stopped and looked at a dog standing on a half-broken skateboard barking at him. "Ahh! The hound of Miami Heat!" He closed the car door and drove off as fast as he could, but he wasn't looking, and he crashed into another car after a few meters. Dogs started pouring out of the car he crashed into, so the dude with sunglasses took off running with the dogs hot on his heels. By then, I decided I'd had enough excitement for the day, and I took off running for home.

Fortunately, nothing crazy happened on the way back home. After I Introduced the parrot to my mom, I went up to my room to figure out what to name my new pet. I had no idea what was a proper name for parrots, so I consulted the book I bought. If you are stuck on what should you name your pet, look at it and the name will come to you! So, I looked at the parrot... I looked some more and stared at it for some time... until a minute later, I noticed my lamp moved. Then, my table moved and, suddenly, every single object in the room started swirling around like a giant, object whirlpool. The parrot started floating and speaking this poem in a raspy voice:

"You are brave, in your heart, But you cannot stand being apart.

When the time comes, you will stand high, Only then will you fail to die."

Then, everything returned to their original position, and magical sunglasses appeared on the parrot's eyes. As it flew out the window, it started pooping thousand-dollar bills. After I regained consciousness, I knew what I would call the parrot: Cassandra, the Greek prophetess.

The Two Restaurants

One of the most important aspects of human life is food. We eat food for fun. We eat food when we are hungry. We eat to survive. Of course, we have evolved past our primitive ways and now get our food from farms, supermarkets, and restaurants. I have two restaurants that are my personal favorites. They are Il Fico and Over Easy. Let me describe to you three ways how the two restaurants are different from each other.

The first and most visible difference is their location. Il Fico is located at the popular new mall K11. It is on the first floor underground and is among one of the many restaurants along it's "street." Over Easy, on the other hand, is located at Canton Place and is one of the few restaurants on the outer rim of the plaza. Those differences are one of the main ways the two restaurants are different.

When comparing, I came across another difference between the two restaurants: the staff at Il Fico are friendly towards customers and often like to socialize with them, and the staff at Over Easy is shy and usually just takes your order and goes away. Besides, the staff at Il Fico can speak English with Chinese, but the staff at Over Easy can only speak Chinese.

Another difference between the two restaurants is the way meals are served. At Il Fico, there is a large selection of appetizers, main meals, soups, and drinks. At Over Easy, there are only main meals, drinks, and salads. Also, at Il Fico, they serve bread and sauce before any meals come up in case you are hungry.

These are the differences between the two restaurants. This is not a contest, so I will let you judge which you think you would like most. This compare and contrast was done so that others can find out which restaurant they like. Do you like grilled steak? Or, do you like Ramen better? It is entirely up to you.

Part III

An Open Letter To Parents

The Importance of Parental Involvement in A Child's Education.

Most children have two main educators in life: their parents and their teachers. Therefore, it is most important to write this letter to parents who seek to improve the academic outcomes for their children by remaining an active influence in their child's life and beyond the classroom.

Some parents may think by reading the essays in this book prepared by our sons, Howie and Lucien, their writing skills were always proficient. The writing process was developed over time and involved many stages. So, you might be thinking that your child, albeit bright, may still manage to have fear when it comes to writing.

Moreover, you might not be sure of the many ways parental involvement can be exercised in school activities your children are involved with. One thing is for certain: parental involvement is important and ongoing. Below we have provided an annotated list of activities that we have done to stay actively involved in our child's education during the school day, after the school day, on cultural and traditional holidays, and for travel.

During the School Day:

- I go to the school library every week to check out new books, talk to the Librarian to get her recommendation on books, and read book introductions before choosing books for my child.

- Read-aloud with my child every day before grade one.

- Regular reading time every day: one to two hours reading time every day throughout elementary.

- Discuss the Theme, Main Idea, Background, and Author's Motivation with my child.

- Play second-guess game with child: guess the ending of the story; what would happen if you switched characters; or, if you were the author, what would the ending be?

- Participate in each year's school Book Battle.

- Write Book Recommendation for school library.

After the School Day:

- Surround children with books at home; it's at his hands, and the reading area is very cozy.

- Let the child choose what he/she reads; meanwhile, encourage him/her to read a variety of different types of books.

- Borrow books from good reader friends.

- Encourage child to read to his/he younger siblings or friends.

- Read the interesting part of the book to him/her to boost their interest in reading books with higher reading levels.

- Share with my child the book I'm reading (book title, content, and illustration).

- Encourage children to write a book review and a movie review .

- Watch TED talk, BBC Nature Documentary, and/or famous speeches together.

- Watch movie and music developed from the book. (i.e. Harry Potter, Matilda)

Cultural and Traditional Holidays:

- Re-write lyrics with traditional holiday song melody.

- Read to child holiday-related stories, i.e. Halloween stories, Bible stories, Chinese New Year stories, Dragon Boat Festival stories.

- Write poems or riddles based on the holiday theme, i.e. write poems related to moon during the Moon Festival; write lantern riddles during the Lantern Festival.

- Make a video with demonstration and speech of how to make festival food or decoration, and share it with friends (i.e. How to make dumplings or How to make Chinese origami for the Chinese New Year)

Travel

- Use technology to increase self-esteem.

- Use e-reader during long-distance travel. (i.e. Kindle)

- Always have one to two books in a backpack; read it during all waiting time.

- Include bookstores, libraries, and museums into the travel plan/ itinerary.

- Visit favorite author's school, home, coffee shop to build an intimate connection.

- Encourage children to write a journal about interesting topics when traveling.

- Write postcards to friends or siblings during travel.

Advice To Teachers

Dear teachers around the world,

If you are reading this, it means that our book publishing has been successful. I hope you like our book. If your students are having trouble with writing, instead of immediately giving them a topic to write about, you should let them expand their creativity; let them free write. After they finish their story, you can check it and see what they can improve. The benefits of doing this instead of straight-up writing are that they are describing something they know, giving them more interest in what they are writing about. As they are writing, you could also ask them to add a picture to go with it, so they know what they are describing. When they are finished editing, you can ask them to write about a particular topic.

Teachers, if they don't know how to write something, you can ask them to see their own writing—how they wrote it before. Although I don't have as much teaching experience compared to you, from a student's perspective, I think this idea is decent, and I hope my suggestions will help.

Best wishes,

Howie

Advice To Teachers

Dear Teachers,

Do you have trouble getting your students to write? Do they think a non-fiction book is too boring and a realistic fiction book has no dragons and princesses? I had the same trouble. too. I didn't like doing realistic fiction and non-fiction articles had too much research for my liking. My teachers struggled for a bit, then realized the easiest way to get me to write was to let me write whatever I wanted. I bet that's the same case for your students!

I suggest that you let them write freely, whether it's about a video game or their favorite toy comes to life. Just let them write. Slowly push them towards some other forms of writing, and if they think you are pushing them too hard, slow down a little until they are ready to move on. Another way is to let them read whatever they want—I mean whatever they want. Reading and writing are quite similar, so students may be inspired to write by reading. If you like reading yourself, you can do something called read-aloud. It's when you read a book to your students. I recommend this a lot, and if you do want to pick this one, be sure to pick a good book! A final way to help your students write is to encourage them to start a newspaper. One girl at my school started a newspaper, and it encouraged quite a few kids to join who started to like writing. Tell your students to be creative with the newspaper. It probably could even be fake news! I think this is a good way to help your students write. These tips have helped me in the past. That is how I came to this spot today, writing this book. I hope you find them helpful to you, too.

Best wishes,

Lucien Z.

Bio Of Howie

Howie Chan is an 11-years-old fifth-grade student, moving up to sixth grade in August 2019. He lives in Guangzhou, the third-largest capital city in China. His love of writing began in Kindergarten where he wrote his first book, called "POLICE." Howie has evolved into a young writer with a great passion for drawing and creating comic book characters about heroes and villains. Other people find him pleasing to work with. He likes basketball, playing Go, reading, playing video games, and watching movies—all things that give him ideas for what to write next.

Bio Of Lucien

As the co-author of the book, The Courage to Write, Lucien Zeng is 11 years old in 2019. He is a student at the American School of Guangzhou. Lucien started his writing career in first grade. His first published work was a poem entitled "Batman." Lucien was only six years old at the time. Three years later, Lucien continues to write and engage in Public Speaking activities, as well as enlighten the minds of other young readers with his sense of wit, charm, and his humanitarian activities for school children living in Laos, located in Southeast Asia, and hopes to do the same in other parts of the world. Right now, he is living in Guangzhou, the third-largest capital city in China. He will be moving to Canada in the near future and hopes to get a pet there because he really likes animals.